How many sleeping bunnies do you count?

6 7 8

1 ● one

How many bunnies?   1   2   3

Trace 1. Write 1.

Trace **one**. Write **one**.

one

Draw a line from 1 to each group of 1 thing.

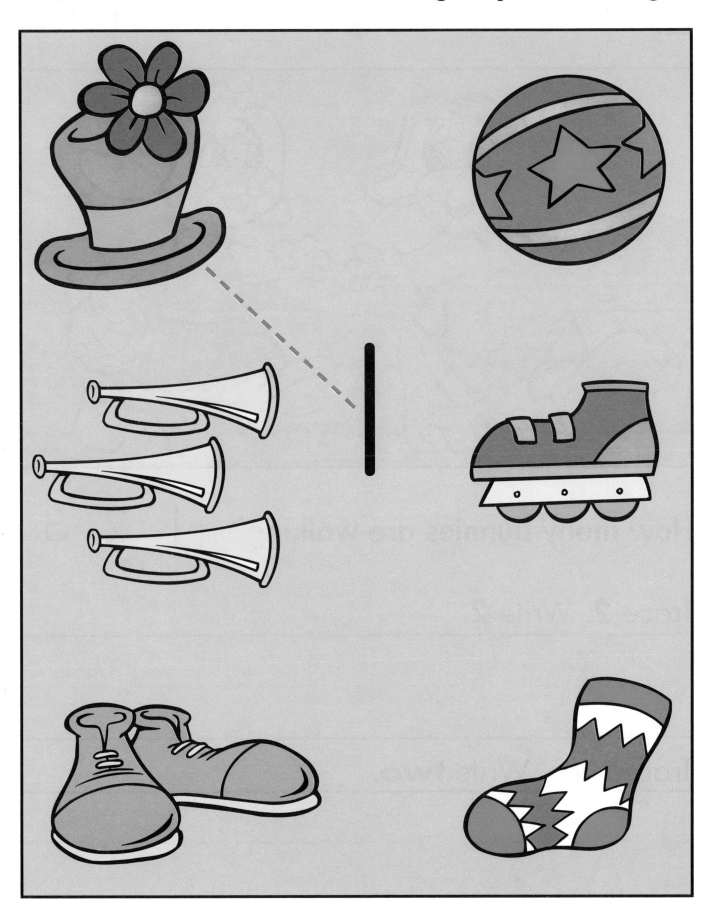

2 : two

How many bunnies are walking? 1 2 3

Trace **2**. Write **2**.

2

Trace **two**. Write **two**.

two

Find and circle 2:

3 three

How many bunnies are playing? 1 2 3

Trace **3**. Write **3**.

3

Trace **three**. Write **three**.

three

Follow the path of **3**s to help get the bunny to his friends.

4   four

How many bunnies are running?   3   4   5

Trace 4. Write 4.

4

Trace **four**. Write **four**.

four

Draw a line to match each number with the correct group of things.

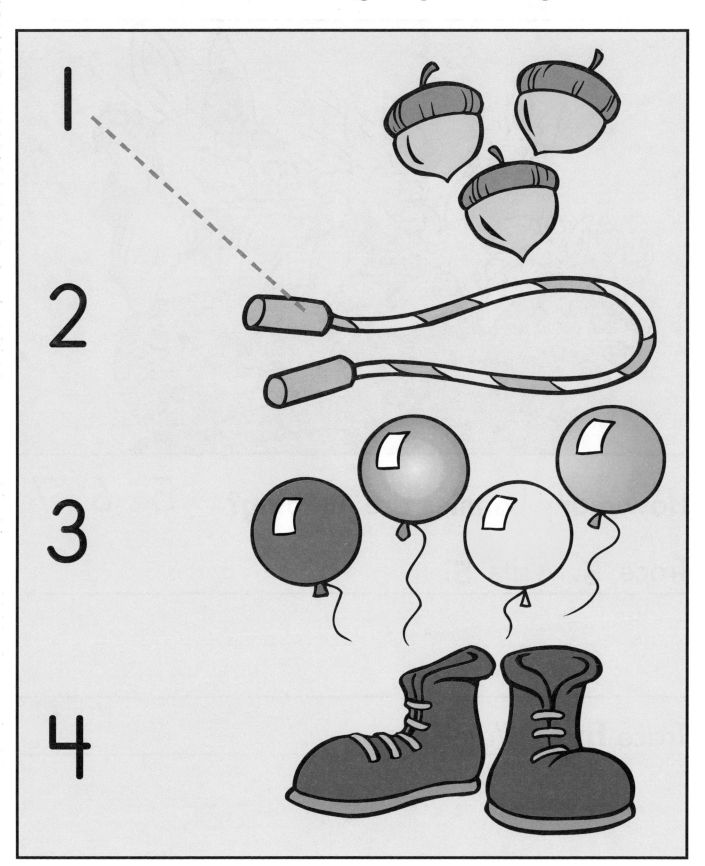

5

five

How many bunnies are jumping?   5   6   7

Trace **5**. Write **5**.

5

Trace **five**. Write **five**.

five

Circle the groups that have **5** things.

6  six

How many are playing hide-and-seek? 6 7 8

Trace **6**. Write **6**.

6

Trace **six**. Write **six**.

six

Use the code to color the picture.

7  seven

How many will have juice?   6 7 8

Trace **7**. Write **7**.

7

Trace **seven**. Write **seven**.

seven

Draw a line from **7** to each group of **7** things.

15

8

eight

How many bunnies are sleeping? 7 8 9

Trace **8**. Write **8**.

8

Trace **eight**. Write **eight**.

eight

Draw a line to match each number with the correct group of things.

5

6

7

8

q

nine

How many bunnies are singing? 9 10 11

Trace **9**. Write **9**.

q

Trace **nine**. Write **nine**.

nine

Use the code to color the picture.

4	5	6	7	8	9
red	blue	green	yellow	brown	orange

10 ten

How many bunnies read together? 9 10 11

Trace **10**. Write **10**.

Trace **ten**. Write **ten**.

ten

Connect the dots from 1 to 10
to finish the picture.

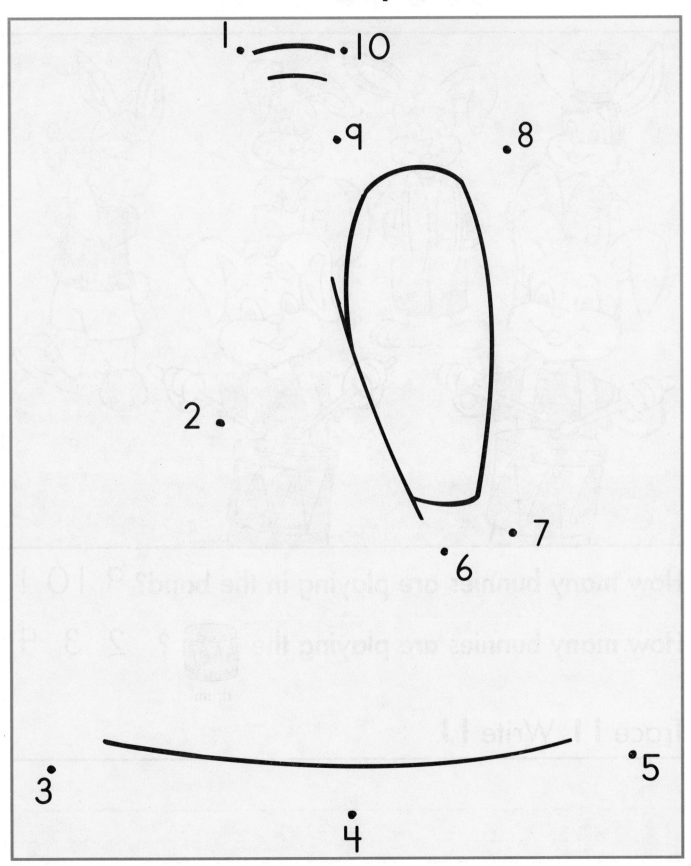

11   ●●●●●   eleven

How many bunnies are playing in the band? 9   10   11

How many bunnies are playing the **?**   2   3   4

drum

Trace **11**. Write **11**.

How many bunnies are playing the ?   2   3   4

cymbals

How many bunnies are playing the ![flute] ?   5   6   7

flute

Trace **eleven**. Write **eleven**.

eleven

12

twelve

How many bunnies are having fun? 10 11 12

How many bunnies have red shoes? 2 3 4

Trace **12**. Write **12**.

12

How many bunnies are wearing a hat?   3   4   5

How many bunnies have a pink shirt?   2   3   4

Trace **twelve**. Write **twelve**.

twelve

Draw a line to match each number
with the correct group of things.

9

10

11

12

Connect the dots from 1 to 12
to complete the picture.

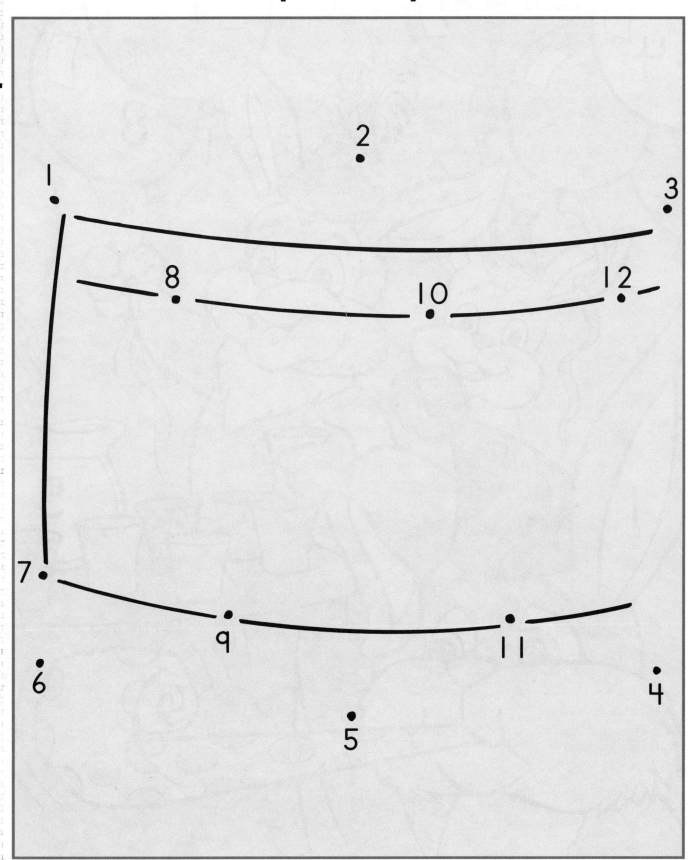

Find and circle the numbers from 1 to 12.

Read the numbers on each envelope. Draw a line to deliver each envelope to the right house.

Read the words. Circle the number that matches the number word.

five	6	0	3	(5)
six	1	6	2	8
seven	0	6	7	3
eight	8	2	4	9
nine	9	2	8	5

Family Fun Activities

These activities will provide review of the concepts
explored on the workbook pages.

1. Counting Practice
As you go about daily activities with your child, look for opportunities to count
things. As you stand in line at the grocery store, count the number of eggs
in the egg carton, the number of apples in the bag, and the number of people
waiting to check out.

2. Make a Counting Book
Staple together 12 pages of blank paper. Encourage your child to write a number
on each page. Ask the child to name each number and draw a corresponding
number of objects on the page. Do not expect the child to complete the number
pages in order or in one sitting. Instead, consider this a long-term project and add a
number page each time your child becomes familiar with the number and the amount
of objects associated with that number. To review the numbers, ask your child to
share the book with others.

3. Concentration
Using a deck of cards with the face cards removed, play a number concentration
game. Begin with the numbers one through six of two suits. Explain to your child
that an ace is a one. Spread the cards face down on a table. Ask the child to turn
over two cards. If the cards match, the child keeps the cards and draws again.
If the cards do not match, they are turned back over and play passes to the next
player. When all the cards are matched, the player with the most cards wins. Add
additional numbers as your child displays success at matching pairs.

4. Number Walk
Help your child discover all the ways numbers are used in
everyday life. Look for numbers on license plates, mailboxes,
houses, mail, clocks, money, etc. Discuss how the numbers are
used and what would happen if there were no numbers.

5. Visit the Library
Go to your local library and help your child register for a library
card. Ask the children's librarian to recommend books that reinforce numbers. Help the child find books that use numbers in the
title, such as "The Three Bears" or "The Three Little Pigs." Look for
songs and poems that reinforce number concepts such as "One,
Two, Buckle My Shoe" and "10 Little Monkeys Lying In Bed."

6. Reward Stickers
Use reward stickers to celebrate a job well done. You or your child can choose
when to place a sticker on a specific page. Use a sticker as a reward when
your child completes a page that requires extra care or is a little more difficult.
Your child can choose to place stickers on pages he or she is proud of completing.